2005

Dear Lindsay,

'Tis the season
to nuke insects'
♫ ♪ ♪

Yr a Pal

♡

Charlee
XXX
☺

THE FOREST
A TRUE STORY

HAPPENED YESTERDAY   DRAWN JUNE 17, 1989

THE RAIN SOAKED ME IN THE FOREST

VINES TRIPPED MY FEET

BRANCHES BORED MY EYES

THE FOREST

MOUNT EMBLEM CEMETARY   BENSENVILLE?, ILLINOIS...

MEN OUT ON THE HILL WERE DIGGING GRAVES IN THE RAIN

This is still The Forest

INCENSE WAS POURING OUT OF SOMEWHERE

The Forest

MOUNT EMBLEM— ILLINOIS' MOST BEAUTIFUL CEMETARY

John Porcellino

I FLED

DIARY OF A
MOSQUITO
ABATEMENT MAN

JOHN PORCELLINO

LA
MANO

Diary of a Mosquito Abatement Man
by John Porcellino

Published by La Mano:
P.O. Box 580828
Minneapolis, MN 55458 USA

www.lamano21.com

Publisher: Zak Sally

Layout and Design: Tom Devlin and John Porcellino

ISBN 0-976-5255-0-X
First Printing: January 2005

Portions of this book originally appeared in
King-Cat Comics and Stories, 1989–1999

For more information please visit
www.king-cat.net

Forge.

this book is dedicated,
with love, to mosquitoes,
men, women, and all
beings ; grasses, rocks,
fences and sky.

Introduction

In 1979, when I was 10 years old, my family and I moved from the city of Chicago to the Northwest suburbs—to a little town called Hoffman Estates. At the time, this area stood at the very edge of Chicagoland's western sprawl, and beyond the cookie cutter subdivisions and mini-marts laid a great expanse of forests, fields, and wetlands—a veritable wilderness, to a boy raised in the city.

My friends and I spent most of our time out there, in the woods—exploring the many grassy hillsides, old farmers' fields, creek banks and ponds that we came across. I felt embraced by the natural world, and as the years went by, although I wasn't conscious of it at the time, my relationship with nature began to take on a deep and special meaning to me. During my teenage years, despite my angst, I felt connected with nature, with something bigger, even in my solitude.

Occasionally, when we were out on our excursions, my friends and I would come across certain young men working in the field. Their yellow pickup trucks were parked on the side of the road. You'd see them there in tall rubber boots, crossing a flooded field; or taking water samples along the edge of a marsh with long-handled dippers—having, by the looks of it, a grand old time.

It turned out they were workers from the county's Mosquito Abatement program (Due to the mosquito's potential for transmitting certain diseases, along with the high annoyance levels their biting can cause, many municipalities conduct mosquito abatement operations as a matter of Public Health). We called these guys "mosquito men"—and in our minds we made it out to be just about the best job in the world. Basically, they got paid to do what we did for fun: stomp around in old swamps, investigate cattails, and explore our beloved ditches and ponds.

So, in the spring of 1989, when I was 20 years old, and I found out that the local mosquito control company was hiring, I got right in line. They signed me up and made me a "field inspector"—they gave me a map and a dipper and a sack full of Bti*. They got me licensed as a pesticide applicator and turned me loose on the ditches and swamps of Chicagoland.

The job of a field inspector was fairly simple—to find the places where mosquitoes were breeding (ditches, sinkholes, marshes and discarded old tires, for instance)—any place, really, that could hold water for more than a few days—and when you find them, you kill them.

It was a good job. You got to spend the summer outdoors, in the fresh air, with no boss looking over your shoulder. You got to go places you weren't

*Bacillus thuringiensis israelensis, a microbial larvicide

supposed to go, see things you weren't supposed to see (as a mosquito man you looked official even when you weren't, and you got good at hopping fences).

Even though I was responsible for the deaths of untold numbers of mosquitoes, I had no moral reservations about what I did. The company made sure we were all educated about the deadly diseases mosquitoes transmitted, and the pesticides we used, we were told, were "safe." (My boss even suggested that a peanut butter and Bti sandwich wouldn't taste that great, but would be totally harmless for a human to eat). In any case, I just didn't think about it that much.

So, I worked through that first season, and the next year, when I needed a job, I called the mosquito company again. They rehired me—this time as a "ULV (Ultra Low Volume) spray technician." This job consisted of driving around the suburbs all night long, in a flatbed pickup truck, spraying a pesticide fog into the air that killed adult mosquitoes (but was otherwise "safe.")

As a spray rig driver I worked six days a week, often pulling twelve hour shifts. We worked from dusk until dawn every night, and sometimes clocked 72 hours in a week. I didn't mind—that's a lot of overtime—but it was enough to make you go a little crazy after a while.

You'd show up for work, get your assignment, and drive out to the route's go point, start spraying. As you sprayed, you drove 12 mph, no faster, no slower. (They had monitoring devices in each truck that recorded your speed at all times). Just so you know, 12 mph works out to be 1 mile every five minutes, or 2/10 of a mile every minute. Some of the routes were well over thirty miles long. Let's just say—when you've been driving 12 mph, alone, in the pitch black for 3 or 4 hours straight, your mind can begin to play tricks on you.

Still, when I moved to Colorado in 1992, and found out there was a mosquito company in town, I went and applied for a job there, too.

It was a good job. In Colorado, I worked again as a field inspector and occasionally drove the spray rig at night. After a few years of this, working my way up the company ladder, I started to think that maybe I could make a "career" of it… Then, one day, I got sick—and overnight, everything changed.

• • • • •

During those years I worked as a mosquito man, in Chicago and Denver, I documented some of my on-the-job exploits and travails in comic book form, and published them in my little magazine King-Cat Comics. The book you now hold collects all the mosquito related stories that appeared in King-Cat, from 1989 to 1999, as well as new material done specifically for this volume.

I've changed a lot as a person since these stories first appeared, and to be honest, I feel pretty embarrassed about some of them. When I started King-Cat, I felt no editorial restraints at all—in working on a story there was no planning beforehand, and no second guessing afterwards. Consequently, some of the early strips are pretty crude, both in terms of execution and content. In the process of putting this book together, I was really tempted to go back in and start cutting things out and redrawing/revising. But in the end, in an effort to be as honest as possible, I've decided to let them all stand as they were when originally published. Please bear this in mind as you read these old strips.

Lastly, I wanted to say—I'm certainly not proud of what I did as a mosquito man; in fact, I feel downright ashamed. I just wanted to share this story of mine, in the hopes that somebody out there might be able to get something positive out of it.

Thanks for listening!

Sincerely,

John Porcellino
San Francisco, CA
December 2004

THE FIRST SEASON

FUCKIN THINGS...
I'VE COME TO KILL YOUR CHILDREN!
ZZZ
ZZZ
ZZZ
DIARY OF A MOSQUITO ABATEMENT MAN

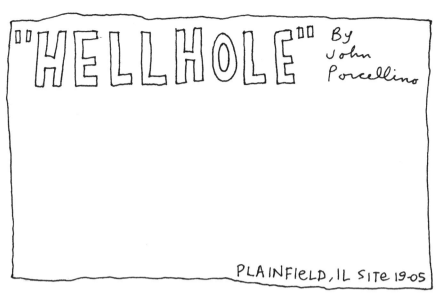

"HELLHOLE" By John Porcellino

PLAINFIELD, IL SITE 19-05

THINGS THAT SHOULD NOT BE:

THORNS ON PLANTS

KILLING VINES

BARBED WIRE

TICKS

AND MOSQUITOES

THE PLACE IS A HELL-HOLE - A FESTERING MOSQUITO PARADISE. BUT I NEED PROOF- A LARVA SAMPLE...

5 BIG LARVAE, 2 PUPAE — IT'S ALL THE EVIDENCE I NEED

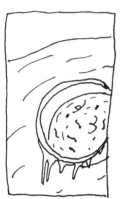

GETTING THE SAMPLE FROM THE DIPPER TO THE SAMPLE CUP REQUIRES 2 HANDS- I CAN'T SWAT 'EM OFF. I'M GETTING BITTEN LIKE NOBODY'S BUSINESS...

THREE

I DUMP THE CUP IN MY SACK AND MAKE MY escape...

FOR ONCE, THE PLANTS ARE ON MY SIDE...

I FILL OUT MY REPORT, LOAD UP WITH PESTICIDE. RETURNING TO THE HOLE, I DUMP $\frac{1}{2}$ A POUND OF BTI. THEY'LL BE DEAD WITHIN 24 HOURS.

The End

"SCOTT" By John Porcellino

WAUKEGAN, IL SITE 24-03

I WAS CHECKING A DITCH ALONG THE E., J., & E. RY. ABOUT 2 P.M.

* ACTUALLY, IT'S ABOUT 45 MILES - ed.

I PRETENDED TO CHECK THE WATER SOME MORE. HE STOOD UP BY THE TRACKS. HE WAS TRYING TO FIGURE OUT HOW TO ASK ME FOR A RIDE...

SEX ON THE BEACH

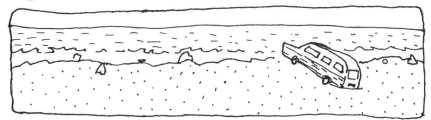

THEY WERE IN A COUNTRY SQUIRE, PARKED AT THE BEACH.

THEY WERE GREASY, IN THE FRONT SEAT. SHE WAS GAP TOOTHED, ZITTED.

THEY MOVED FAST AT FIRST, HER HEAD BANGED THE DOOR.

I WAS REPULSED AND FASCINATED AT THE SAME TIME. THEY SLOWED AND FINISHED. HE OPENED HIS EYES AND LOOKED RIGHT AT ME, FLASHING A GOLD-CAPPED SMILE.

HER LEGS WENT OUT THE WINDOW TO PULL HER UNDERWEAR AND JEANS BACK ON.

THEY DROVE AWAY, LAUGHING...

HAPPENED AT COM-ED BEACH WAUKEGAN, IL. John P. August 2, 1989 (Drawn)

"A WHOLE WORLD IN A DROP OF WATER"

MAYFLY LARVA

FROG BUG

FUNNY YELLOW BUG

FLATWORM

LITTLE SEE-THRU BUG

WORMS

TADPOLE

MOSQUITO LARVAE

MOSQUITO PUPA

LITTLE BABY CRAYFISH

BABY FISH

WATER WHIRLIES

CUBA TWP. SITE 14-04

MORE OF THE DIARY OF A MOSQUITO ABATEMENT MAN.

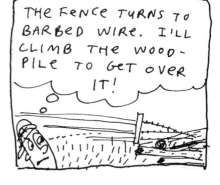

I GOT STUNG 15 TIMES THAT DAY BY A NEST OF YELLOW JACKETS IN CUBA TOWNSHIP, IL.

The End

John Porcellino

THE SECOND SEASON

CHANNAHON

MORE: DIARY OF A MOSQUITO ABATEMENT MAN.

I WAS SHOOTING DOWN RT. 30 INTO PLAINFIELD... THIS

WAS A FEW WEEKS AFTER THE TORNADO HIT.

THERE WAS UTTER DESTRUCTION. THE FEW TREE TRUNKS THAT STOOD WERE STRIPPED OF ALL

THEIR BRANCHES. IT SMELLED LIKE BURNING...

A GROUP HUDDLED UNDER A TENT, LIT BY KERO-

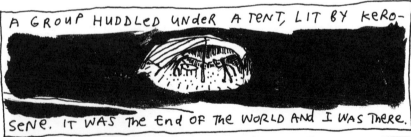

SENE. IT WAS THE END OF THE WORLD AND I WAS THERE.

IN A SHORT WHILE I DROPPED INTO THE CANAL ZONE.

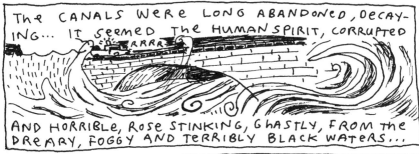

THE CANALS WERE LONG ABANDONED, DECAYING... IT SEEMED THE HUMAN SPIRIT, CORRUPTED

AND HORRIBLE, ROSE STINKING, GHASTLY, FROM THE DREARY, FOGGY AND TERRIBLY BLACK WATERS...

A FEELING OF PURE DREAD WASHED OVER ME AS I

CROSSED THE ONE LANE BRIDGE INTO CHANNAHON.

AT 12 MPH, THIS TERROR IS MAGNIFIED BY THE HORRIBLE SLOWNESS... WHO KNOWS WHAT GOES ON

IN THESE BACKWOODS SHITHOLES? WHAT MONSTERS THESE QUEASY BLACK WATERS HAD SPAWNED?

INTO TOWN, THE ROUTE TOOK ME DOWN CANAL ST.

PAST ROWS OF SHITTY, DELAPIDATED SHACKS.

IN THE LIT WINDOW OF ONE, A BEAUTIFUL GIRL SAT DOING HOMEWORK. AT THE ROAR OF THE

FOGGER, SHE LOOKED UP. I SWEAR TO GOD, OUR EYES LOCKED.

10 MINUTES LATER, WHAT I ASSUME WAS CHANNA-HON'S ONLY SQUAD CAR SCREAMED PAST, LIGHTS FLASHING. IN THE DISTANCE FIRE SIRENS WAILED.

IT IMMEDIATELY SEEMED CERTAIN TO ME THAT THE GIRL'S HOUSE WAS BURNING. I BROKE OFF THE ROUTE AND HEADED TO CANAL ST... THE ROAD WAS FILLED WITH EMERGENCY VEHICLES... IT WAS THE

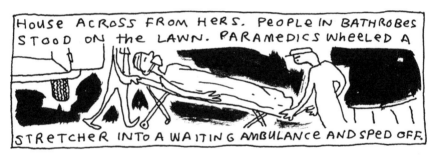

HOUSE ACROSS FROM HERS. PEOPLE IN BATHROBES STOOD ON THE LAWN. PARAMEDICS WHEELED A STRETCHER INTO A WAITING AMBULANCE AND SPED OFF.

I DROVE PAST HER HOUSE AGAIN. THE LIGHT IN HER WINDOW WAS OUT. I GOT BACK ON THE ROUTE

AND FINISHED UP THE TOWN. GETTING OUT OF THE TRUCK ON A BLACK WOODED ROAD TO SHUT THE FOGGER OFF, I NEARLY DIED OF PURE FEAR.

T.E.

CHEMICAL PLANT / ANOTHER WORLD

MORE: DIARY OF A MOSQUITO ABATEMENT MAN

THE ROUTE AFTER CHANNAHON WAS THE
AMALGAMATED* CHEMICAL PLANT, A FEW MILES
DOWN THE HIGHWAY...   *NOT THEIR REAL NAME, ed.

I HAD TO BE THERE
at A CERTAIN TIME...
THE GUARD WAVED ME
IN...

I DROVE UP THE LONG,
DARK ENTRY ROAD
TOWARD THE GO-POINT...

UP AHEAD, THE PLANT ROSE OMINOUSLY
OUT OF THE NIGHT--

--A FLOOD-LIT, OPEN-AIR CITY OF PIPES, WIRES, SCAFFOLDING TOWERS and CATWALKS

I GOT TO THE GO-POINT and STARTED THE ROUTE

...DRIVING TWELVE MILES an HOUR THROUGH THE MAZE-LIKE COMPOUND

DOWN WEIRD STREETS THAT CUT THROUGH THE JUNGLE OF MACHINERY...

WEIRD STREETS WITH NAMES LIKE "TECHNOLOGY", "OXYGEN"--

PROGRESS WY

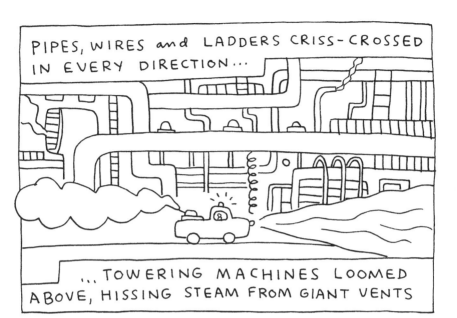

PIPES, WIRES and LADDERS CRISS-CROSSED IN EVERY DIRECTION...

...TOWERING MACHINES LOOMED ABOVE, HISSING STEAM FROM GIANT VENTS

ADDING TO THE SURREAL EFFECT WAS THE FACT THAT EVEN THOUGH IT WAS 2AM OR SO, EVERPRESENT FLOOD-LIGHTS LIT THE PLACE AS BRIGHT AS DAY-- MAYBE BRIGHTER-- WITH A COLD, UN-NATURAL, SHADOWLESS LIGHT...

NOW and THEN I ACTUALLY SAW A HUMAN BEING -- IN A CHEM-SUIT and HARD HAT -- EXAMINING A DIAL...

OR GLIDING ALONG EERILY ON A BICYCLE, SILENT AGAINST THE DRONE OF GENERATORS, PUMPS and FANS

THE WHOLE SPECTACLE SEEMED SO UNREAL - SO BIZARRE...

THE TWO STORY KNOTS OF WIRES and CONDUIT

(HAPPENED: FALL, 1990) DRAWN: John Porcellino, MAY 2004

MY DAD SPENT CONVENTION TIME IN LISLE, ILLINOIS RIGHT WHERE I WORKED AS

A MOSQUITO ABATEMENT MAN. THIS WAS BEFORE I KNEW ANYTHING. NOW I AM DRUNK.

NOV 15 1990

1 A.M.

John Porcellino, drunk.

I GLANCE AT A PENCIL WHICH READS "HOLIDAY INN, CROWNE PLAZA ® 3000 WARRENVILLE ROAD □ LISLE, IL 60532

□ (312) 505-1000" AND I REALIZE I GOT THIS PENCIL FROM MY DAD WHO WAS AT

A CONVENTION IN LISLE, ILL. WHERE I DID MOSQUITO ABATE-MENT WORK.

I QUESTION WHY MY LIFE IS SEEN THROUGH THESE EYES WHY I AM LIKE THIS IF 'T IS GOOD OR BAD.

THE DENVER YEARS

fuck

"NIVER II" IS A Shithole DItch that Runs paRallel to the FARMER'S HighLine canal in Westminster...

I gRudgingly gRabbed my dippeR and slid down the slope, oveR twigs, thorns and bRanches in my face.

Fuckin Shit

Stepping towaRd the seweR mouth, the leaves Rustled and a squiRRel leapt out of them onto a tRee tRunk.

I squatted down and watched him. He hung off the tRee with his foRelegs only, the Rest of his body hanging fRee

?

Suddenly he flung himself to anotheR bRanch and balanced himself on his aRmpits, eyeing me neRvously...

It was then that I Realized his hind quaRteRs weRe paRalyzed...

His chest pounded with feaR

I Backed away slowly and headed up the slope

When I Reached the Road a Mini-Van swept past...

In the passenger seat was a young girl of about 13 years...

She was crying her eyes out.

happened: W/W #23 NIVER II. Drawn August 14, 1994

ASPARAGUS

MORE: DIARY OF A MOSQUITO ABATEMENT MAN

SPRING 2004
SAN FRANCISCO, CALIF.

ONE MORNING I WAS
GETTING READY FOR WORK...

IF I CLEAN THE
ASPARAGUS NOW,
IT'LL BE READY TO
COOK WHEN I
GET HOME

and I REMEMBERED
THE FIRST TIME I EVER
TASTED ASPARAGUS...

IT WAS IN THE SPRING,
PROBABLY 1995 OR SO--

RICK and I WERE IN BOULDER COUNTY, CHECKING
A DITCH THAT RAN ALONG BEHIND THE SCHOOL
DISTRICT BUILDING...

HEY!

ASPARAGUS!!

NOW WE'LL HAVE TO REMEMBER WHERE THIS SPOT IS, and COME BACK NEXT YEAR, TOO!

HUH?

RICK EXPLAINED...

WE WERE LUCKY TO FIND ASPARAGUS WHEN IT'S STILL SHOOTS-- LIKE THESE...

USUALLY YOU DON'T SEE IT TILL IT'S BLOOMED and GONE TO SEED... IT LOOKS LIKE A CROSS BETWEEN A FERN and A CHRISTMAS TREE...

BUT BY THEN IT'S TOO WOODY TO EAT...

SO IF YOU EVER SEE A BIG ASPARAGUS BUSH, REMEMBER WHERE IT IS, and COME BACK THE NEXT YEAR...

THERE'LL BE SHOOTS all AROUND IT-- and as LONG AS YOU KEEP PICKING THEM, THEY'LL KEEP SHOOTING UP!

WAUKEGAN

When I was a Mosquito Man back in Illinois, one of my regular routes was up in Waukegan, along Lake Michigan. This was in the summer of 1989.

Waukegan was a great place to work. For starters it was about an hour away from the Mosquito office, so travelling there and back effectively shaved two hours off each workday. Plus it was just a neat old city, kind of crumbling and derelict but with a unique energy and mystery to it.

Through the center of town ran a deep, craggy ravine and I spent days exploring it. Stumbling down the steep walls, hopping over old mossy logs and rocks, till I got to the bottom where a beautiful rocky stream ran. I'd slosh down the middle in my rubber boots, kicking at the water. Even on the lousiest hot summer day it was always cool and fresh down there, moss and logs and clean, cold water.

Where the stream crossed under Washington St. there was a cool old stone tunnel and I'd splash through there where it was colder and deeper and I was always afraid I was gonna get bit by a rat.

Then the ravine opened up and there was more sunshine and it came out into Roosevelt Park where it drained a bunch of nasty lagoons. I say nasty cuz they were muddy and smelled like shit and there were always huge dead carp rotting on the shore.

One time I came into Roosevelt Park the back way, where the stream begins, pouring out of a concrete drain pipe in a suburban ranch-house neighborhood. I slid down the wooded slope toward the water when I was overpowered by the stench of death. And there it was: an old plastic garbage bag stretched and torn on the slope, with a dead black dog bulging out of the holes.

Another place I'd hang out a lot was the ComEd Beach on the lakefront. In the very northeast corner of town was an enormous old power plant rising out of the Lake. Commonwealth Edison (the power company) had made the beach there accessible to the public so working stiffs like me could have a view with our brown bag lunches. The shoreline here was pretty rocky and I used to sit out on the rocks and eat and watch the waves. It was a good place.

One time I pulled up to the beach and was getting my lunch together when I heard strange, rhythmic sounds coming from the car next to me. A pimply white trash girl was leaning out the driver's side window while a greasy, gaptoothed freak of a man fucked her from behind on the front seat. I didn't know what to do so I just sat there and ate my sandwich.

When they were through she stuck her legs out the window and pulled her jeans up. As they drove away laughing the guy looked right at me and smiled a mouthful of gold teeth.

The transcendent Waukegan experience, though, came toward the end of the summer. It was one of those heat stroke Chicago summer days where it's so hot and humid you can barely breathe. But around one in the afternoon the wind began picking up and the sky to the west rolled deep and grey with stormclouds. In a few moments the wind was cold and out of control, knocking over garbage cans, newspapers blowing wild everywhere. I got in my car and headed for the beach.

When I got there the sky over the Lake was steely grey and deep blue. The wind was going crazy, knocking the waves into five foot monsters, breaking them over the rocks, crashing and roaring and foaming.

A couple drunk guys were out on the rocks shouting, but the wind took their voices away. I can still see them there, long hair blowing, shirts unbuttoned and billowing behind them, beers clenched in cold fists. They were leaning into the wind, defying gravity and just frozen in the waves, in the wind, smashing them and all around.

MOUNTAIN SONG

MORE: DIARY OF A MOSQUITO ABATEMENT MAN by John P.

I AM A MOSQUITO MAN BY TRADE - THAT IS, I CRAWL AROUND IN SWAMPS and DITCHES FOR A LIVING, LOOKING FOR MOSQUITOES TO KILL. THIS PARTICULAR THURSDAY MORNING I WAS HEADING UP INTO the MOUNTAINS TO SERVICE OUR SUMMIT COUNTY ACCOUNTS...
EISENHOWER TUNNEL
YOU LOSE the GOOD COUNTRY STATIONS OVER the DIVIDE
"IT'S BLUE TONIGHT and GETTING BLUER..."
FIZZLE
BUT PRETTY SOON I WAS COMING DOWN INTO the LAKE DILLON VALLEY...
STILL SINGING
80 MPH (COASTING)
UTAH
BLUE RIVER VALLEY
LAKE DILLON

and SOON I WAS IN the SECOND VALLEY...

I SQUATTED ON the EDGE OF the POND and PEERED INTO the WATER...

CADDIS FLIES

CADDIS-FLY
LARVAE

THE WEIRD LARVAE OF THE CADDIS FLY BUILDS A PROTECTIVE CASE MADE OF SAND & TWIGS IN WHICH IT HIDES AS IT SCUTTLES ACROSS SILTY POND BOTTOMS.

I HAD NEVER SEEN ONE BEFORE. I WAS ASTOUNDED BY THE COMPLEXITY and CRAFTMANSHIP OF THEIR LITTLE HOMES.

I HUMBLY REALIZED THAT DESPITE ALL MY HUMAN SKILLS and KNOWLEDGE I COULD NEVER CREATE ANYTHING THAT BEAUTIFUL...

SO I MADE MY WAY AROUND the POND TRYING TO CATCH SALAMANDERS IN MY DIPPER

OUT IN THE MUSKEG EAST OF THE POND I HIT PAYDIRT

MOSQUITO LARVAE

NO DICE...

FINALLY I GAVE UP and WENT FOR HELP

DID YOU GUYS KNOW THERE'S A BULL WITH HIS HEAD STUCK IN THE FENCE

WHAT?!

CUTE AS HELL

THIS IS A HORSE →

and HEADED TO SAGE CREEK

SAGE CREEK IS the MOSQUITO MAN'S NIGHTMARE

A STINKING QUAGMIRE—

BREEDING EVERYWHERE...

ADULTS TOO!

ZZZ

BZZ

ZZ

I'M DROPPING the BOMB

I'M KILLING THOUSANDS...

WHEN I EMERGE I AM SWEATY and SCRATCHED TO RIBBONS...

BUT I HAVE WON the BATTLE

DEATH OF A MOSQUITO ABATEMENT MAN

BY JOHN PORCELLINO

IT WAS THE SPRING OF 1996...
I WAS LIVING IN DENVER, COLORADO,
GETTING READY FOR MY NEXT SEASON
AS A MOSQUITO MAN... BUT THIS TIME
AROUND, THINGS WERE DIFFERENT--
(IT HAD ALL STARTED ABOUT A YEAR
PREVIOUSLY...)

ONE NIGHT IN JAN-
UARY '95, I WENT
OUT WITH SOME
FRIENDS - TO SEE A
COUPLE BANDS, and
HAVE A FEW BEERS

AS I OFTEN DID BACK
THEN, I ENDED UP
GETTING TOTALLY
DRUNK...

THE NEXT MORNING I WOKE UP HUNGOVER, WHICH I EXPECTED...

BUT ALSO WITH A PAINFUL FULLNESS and PRESSURE IN MY RIGHT EAR

AFTER A FEW DAYS MY EAR WASN'T BETTER, So I WENT DOWN TO THE CLINIC

IT'S PROBABLY an EAR INFECTION-- TAKE THESE ANTIBIOTICS FOR TEN DAYS...

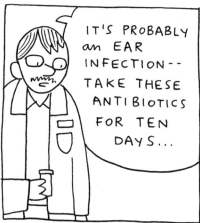

I TOOK THE ANTI- BIOTICS...

and THE NEXT WEEK- END WE all WENT OUT TO A SUPER BOWL PARTY...

ONCE AGAIN, I PROCEEDED TO GET TOTALLY SMASHED

(SOMEHOW, I'D MADE IT THAT FAR IN LIFE WITHOUT ANYONE TELLING ME NOT TO MIX ANTIBIOTICS and BOOZE)

BY THE NEXT MORNING I WAS SERIOUSLY ILL...

AARGH!

BLEEAUGH

I STAYED ON THE COUCH FOR DAYS... I COULDN'T EAT, OR EVEN MOVE, WITHOUT THE NAUSEA TAKING OVER...

THIS ALTERNATED WITH WAVE UPON WAVE OF VIOLENT DIARRHEA...

AFTER SEVERAL DAYS OF THIS, IT OCCURRED TO ME THAT I MIGHT ACTUALLY BE DYING...

I FIGURED I BETTER GET MY HOUSE IN ORDER

I CRAWLED TO THE BOOKSHELF and PICKED OUT THE BIBLE, and a PAPERBACK CALLED HOW THE GREAT RELIGIONS BEGAN*, A BOOK I'D CARRIED AROUND WITH ME FOR MANY YEARS, BUT HAD NEVER READ...

* Joseph Gaer, Signet 1954

I DRAGGED MYSELF BACK TO THE COUCH and STARTED TO READ

WHAT I FOUND IN THE "Religions" BOOK STARTLED and AMAZED ME...

ALL THE WORLD'S RELIGIONS ARE SAYING THE SAME BASIC THING— ONLY FILTERED THROUGH THEIR OWN UNIQUE CULTURAL CIRCUMSTANCES and REFERENCE POINTS!

READING THAT BOOK CHANGED MY LIFE...

I BEGAN STUDYING HINDUISM, BUDDHISM, and RE-EXPLORING MY CHRISTIAN ROOTS...

I RE-READ THE NEW TESTAMENT, WITH NEW EYES, and A NEW MIND

SUDDENLY, I FELT MY LIFE TRANSFORMING

MEANWHILE, THOUGH, MY EAR STILL HURT...

I GUESS THOSE ANTIBIOTICS DIDN'T WORK...

I MADE IT THROUGH THE MOSQUITO SEASON THAT YEAR - BUT THE WHOLE TIME MY EAR WAS PAINFUL and SWOLLEN

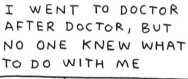

I WENT TO DOCTOR AFTER DOCTOR, BUT NO ONE KNEW WHAT TO DO WITH ME

IT MUST BE AN EAR INFECTION

MAYBE IT'S A SINUS INFECTION...

HAVE YOU EVER CONSIDERED PSYCHOTHERAPY?
*

* THINKS I'm MAKING IT UP

ROUND AFTER ROUND OF TESTS and TREATMENTS OFFERED NO RELIEF...

THAT FALL, I TRIED ACUPUNCTURE, as A LAST DITCH EFFORT...

MIGHT AS WELL TRY...

IT CAN'T HURT...

Pinnow suggested it →

WITHIN TWO OR THREE TREATMENTS, THE PAIN IN MY EAR WAS GONE!!

IT WAS THEN THAT I MADE A STARTLING DISCOVERY...

SLAM!

IT TURNED OUT THAT THE PAIN I WAS EXPERIENCING WAS TRIGGERED BY EXPOSURE TO SOUND...

NER-NEE! NER-NEE!

↑ CAR ALARM

(MY EAR HAD HURT CONTINUOUSLY SINCE JANUARY BECAUSE THAT WHOLE TIME IT HAD BEEN SUBJECTED TO "PAINFUL" SOUNDS WITHOUT EVER HAVING A CHANCE TO RECOVER)

I SUDDENLY FOUND MYSELF IN A WORLD WHERE JUST ABOUT ANYTHING COULD BE A POTENTIAL THREAT--

ROAR!!

HARLEY

--LOUD SOUNDS REALLY HURT--

BUT EVEN EVERYDAY SOUNDS YOU'D NORMALLY THINK OF AS QUIET COULD TRIGGER THE PRESSURE and PAIN TOO...

TURNING OFF LIGHT SWITCH

CLICK

ONE EXPOSURE COULD SEND MY EAR REELING-- FOR ANYWHERE FROM A FEW HOURS TO A FEW WEEKS...

(DROPPED FORK ON PLATE)

CLANK!

OW!

CONSEQUENTLY, MY LIFE BECAME PRETTY WEIRD...

PLUGGING EAR WITH FINGER

FLUSH!

I HAD TO RE-LEARN HOW TO DO THE SIMPLEST TASKS IN A QUIET WAY...

PULLING CAR DOOR CLOSED WITH ELBOW

(:CLICK:)

I WORE EARPLUGS all THE TIME --

IT'S ALL TOO LOUD!!

and I STARTED TO WITHDRAW FROM THE OUTSIDE WORLD...

IN THE OFF-SEASON THAT YEAR, I KEPT UP MY ACUPUNCTURE TREATMENTS

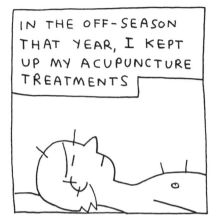

...and I CONTINUED STUDYING THE WORLD'S RELIGIONS...

THINGS WERE CHANGING FAST-- THE SPIRITUAL LONGING WITHIN ME WAS GROWING STRONG-ER and STRONGER

THAT WINTER I BEGAN STUDYING BUDDHISM IN EARNEST

TRYING TO MEDITATE

meow??

I WAS ATTRACTED TO ITS TEACHINGS OF WISDOM & COMPASSION

and ITS STRAIGHTFOR-WARD PRACTICALITY...

THE FIRST SET OF BUDDHIST TEACHINGS IS CALLED

THE FOUR NOBLE TRUTHS...

THE FOUR NOBLE TRUTHS ARE:

1. LIFE IS FRAUGHT WITH SUFFERING, OF ALL KINDS...

2. THE CAUSE of THIS SUFFERING IS SELFISH DESIRE...

3. BY EXTINGUISHING SELFISH DESIRE, ONE CAN ALLEVIATE SUFFERING

and 4. THE WAY TO EXTINGUISH SELFISH DESIRE IS THROUGH A WAY OF LIFE CALLED "THE EIGHTFOLD PATH"

ONE OF THE ASPECTS OF THE EIGHTFOLD PATH IS A CONCEPT CALLED "RIGHT LIVELIHOOD"... IN THE MOST SIMPLE TERMS— CHOOSING AN OCCUPATION THAT IS SPIRITUALLY POSITIVE, NOT NEGATIVE...

AS SOON AS I HEARD THIS, I HAD ONE IMMEDIATE THOUGHT:

BEING A MOSQUITO MAN IS NOT RIGHT LIVELIHOOD!

LOOKING BACK, I THINK I HAD ALWAYS FELT A VAGUE SENSE OF UNEASE ABOUT WHAT I DID FOR A LIVING...

THAT IT WAS MORAL-LY UNJUSTIFIED...

and I WAS ALWAYS TRYING TO RATIONALIZE IT TO MYSELF...

MOSQUITOES BITE PEOPLE...

THEY CARRY DISEASES...

THEY'RE JUST BUGS...

ETC.

ALL AT ONCE, THOSE RATIONALIZATIONS BEGAN TO WITHER...

SUDDENLY, MY JOB JUST SEEMED... WRONG

MEANWHILE, THE NEW MOSQUITO SEASON WAS FAST APPROACHING...

1996

I REALIZED NOW THAT I COULD NO LONGER PERFORM MY DUTIES as a MOSQUITO MAN and STILL KEEP A CLEAN CONSCIENCE...

??

BUT I COULDN'T BRING MYSELF TO QUIT, EITHER

I WENT INTO WORK and SET ABOUT GETTING THINGS READY FOR THE NEW SEASON

PAINTING OVER RUST SPOTS ON THE TRUCKS →

PSSH

I DIDN'T MENTION MY MORAL DILEMMA TO ANYONE...

BUT INSIDE IT WAS TEARING ME APART

WHAT AM I GONNA DO?!?

THIS IS A GOOD JOB... I MAKE GOOD MONEY... I GET FOUR MONTHS OFF EVERY YEAR...

BLAH BLAH BLAH

ON THE OTHER HAND, I HAD HAD SOME SCARY EXPERIENCES ON THE JOB, TOO... LIKE THE TIME I HAD TO "BARRIER SPRAY" SOME RICH PEOPLE'S HOUSE FOR A WEDDING RECEPTION...

STUPID F*CKIN' MILLIONAIRES!! WHAT DID YOU EXPECT?!

RRR

YOU BUILT YOUR HOUSE ON A SWAMP!!

AS I WORKED THAT DAY, THE SPRAY DRIFTED ACROSS ME AGAIN and AGAIN...

BY THE EVENING-TIME, MY FACE and NECK WERE BURNING INTENSELY...

IT LOOKS NORMAL... BUT- AARGH!!

PUTTING ALOE ON MY FACE

WHEN I TOLD MY BOSS WHAT HAPPENED, HE JUST SHRUGGED, and SAID:

SOUNDS LIKE YOU HAD A REACTION...

I HAD SEVERAL OTHER EXPERIENCES LIKE THIS ONE, TOO...

SQUIRT

ALSO, I DON'T THINK ANYONE WHO SPENDS THAT MUCH TIME OUT IN NATURE CAN HELP BUT COME AWAY WITH A SENSE OF WONDER and RESPECT FOR LIFE, and THE NATURAL WORLD...

ONE OF OUR CONTRACTS IN COLORADO WAS WITH BOULDER COUNTY... BOULDER IS A HOTBED OF PROGRESSIVE POLITICS, and HOME TO MANY ENVIRON- MENTAL CAUSES...

EVERY YEAR BEFORE THE NEW SEASON BEGAN WE'D HAVE TO GO IN and MEET WITH THE BOULDER COUNTY OFFICIALS... PUBLIC HEALTH WORKERS and OPEN SPACE and ENVIRONMENTAL RE- SOURCES STAFF...

EVERY YEAR THE OPEN SPACE PEOPLE WOULD DO EVERYTHING THEY COULD TO LIMIT OUR ACCESS TO PUBLIC LAND, and TO RESTRICT WHAT KINDS OF PESTICIDES WE COULD USE, and WHERE... IT ALWAYS ENDED UP IN A BIG ARGUMENT...

THE ALLROY RANCH IS PRISTINE BOBOLINK HABITAT! YOU'RE NOT GOING IN THERE!!

WE HAVE TO DO OUR JOB!!

EVERY YEAR ON THE RIDE HOME I HAD TO LISTEN TO MY BOSS COMPLAIN ABOUT THE "WHACKOS" and THE "ENVIRO-NUTS"

BLAH BLAH BLAH

and EVERY YEAR I FOUND MYSELF AGREEING MORE and MORE WITH "THE ENEMY"...

BUT THEY'VE EXTRAPOLATED THE DATA OVER 50 YEARS — WITH NO SIGN OF DRAGONFLY MORTALITY!

FIFTY YEARS MEANS NOTHING IN THE GRAND SCHEME OF THINGS!!

HE'S RIGHT...

AT THAT YEAR'S MEETING IT WAS QUITE APPARENT... I WAS ON THE WRONG SIDE OF THE TABLE...

BLAH BLAH BLAH!

SO, ALL AT ONCE, I FELT THE WEIGHT OF THESE DIFFERENT ASPECTS OF MY LIFE-- MY HEALTH PROBLEMS, MY SPIRITUAL ASPIRATIONS, MY GROWING ENVIRONMENTAL AWARENESS -- all COMING TOGETHER TO LEAD ME TOWARD ONE INESCAPABLE CONCLUSION: "QUIT YOUR JOB!"

BUT STILL I WENT IN TO WORK...

SWEEP SWEEP

I BUSIED MYSELF WITH LITTLE TASKS WHERE I WOULDN'T HAVE TO HANDLE PESTICIDES...

I DIDN'T WANT TO EVER HAVE TO KILL ANOTHER MOSQUITO

I MANAGED TO PLAY ALONG LIKE THIS FOR A COUPLE OF WEEKS, BUT I KNEW I COULDN'T KEEP UP MY CHARADE MUCH LONGER

ONE DAY I WAS UP IN THE MOUNTAINS, TRAINING A NEW EMPLOYEE...

WE WERE SITTING IN THE TRUCK, EATING LUNCH and DISCUSSING THE JOB... SUDDENLY, SHE TURNED TO ME and SAID:

BUT DON'T YOU EVER FEEL BAD?

DON'T YOU EVER FEEL BAD THAT YOU'RE KILLING ALL THESE INNOCENT CREATURES?

THAT YOU'RE PUTTING ALL THESE CHEMICALS OUT INTO THE ENVIRONMENT?

IS IT REALLY WORTH IT?!

I SAT IN STUNNED SILENCE

AT THAT MOMENT I KNEW IT WAS OVER

I KNEW I WAS NO LONGER A MOSQUITO MAN...

THAT AFTERNOON, WE WERE PLANNING TO TREAT A FLOODED PASTURE - FULL OF THOUSANDS and THOUSANDS OF MOSQUITO LARVAE

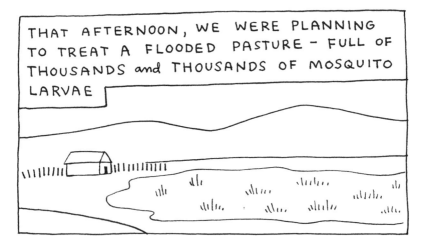

AS THE OTHER WORKERS PREPARED THE PESTICIDE SOLUTION, I WADED THROUGH THE WATER, MUTTERING TO THE LARVAE UNDER MY BREATH:

THEY'RE GOING TO SPRAY SOMETHING IN THE WATER THAT WILL KILL YOU!!

PLEASE-- BE CAREFUL!

BE CAREFUL!!

WHEN THE TIME CAME I DIDN'T KNOW WHAT ELSE TO DO--

I CLAMBERED UP OUT OF THE WATER, ONTO THE EDGE OF THE FIELD...

and WATCHED THE MOSQUITO MEN WEAVE BACK and FORTH WITH THEIR SPRAYERS.

A FEW DAYS LATER I BROKE DOWN IN THE OFFICE — and CONFESSED MY FEELINGS TO MY FRIEND, and CO-WORKER, RICK:

I JUST CAN'T DO IT ANYMORE!!

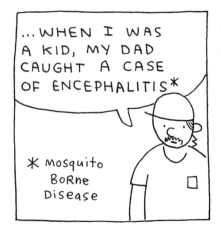

BECAUSE OF THAT EXPERIENCE, I HAVE NO QUALMS ABOUT WHAT I DO HERE...

I TOOK RICK'S STORY TO HEART, BUT FOR ME, THE DIE HAD BEEN CAST...

A DAY OR TWO LATER I ARRANGED A MEETING WITH MY BOSS

WE NEED TO TALK...

WHEN I TOLD HIM I WAS LEAVING, HE WAS SHOCKED -

WHAT?! WHY??

IN ANSWER, I MENTIONED MY EARS...

JOHN PORCELLINO
2003 - 2004

THE OWL

The Owl

Once, when I was a Mosquito Man, my job was to drive the Spray Rig at night. (the Spray Rig is a truck that shoots a chemical fog into the air – this fog kills any bugs it comes into contact with).

One night while spraying, I turned down a dark, forboding country lane. At one point the road entered a thick forest.

There, in the branches up ahead, I saw an enormous Owl. He watched me with Giant Eyes...

I was thrilled to see such a marvelous creature, but I drove slowly past him and continued down the Road.

Suddenly, the Owl appeared over the truck, floating down the windshield and over the hood on silent, outstretched wings.

He soared ahead of me for awhile, illuminated in the headlights, and then he perched again in another tree.

As I passed him the second time, he Repeated this strange flight, gliding over and across the truck, like a Ghost.

This happened several more times as I travelled down the Road, spraying.

At the time I thought it was mysterious and Beautiful— an omen of some sort — But now I see that I was just poisoning Him.

In my life I've done many things that I Regret. I'm sorry I was ever a Mosquito Man.

this concludes the Diary of a Mosquito Abatement Man

1989 — 1999 R.I.P.